TALES FROM THE WORLD OF...
SONIC: GENESIS
FRIENDS AND FATE
WELCOME TO A WHOLE NEW WORLD-- ONE UNIQUE AND BEYOND WHAT YOU KNOW FROM THE SEGA GAMES -- WHERE WE CONTINUE THE ALL-NEW, ALL-DIFFERENT ADVENTURES OF A SPEEDY BLUE HERO NAMED SONIC THE HEDGEHOG!
D0943131
WRITER: IAN FLYNN
PENCIL BREAKDOWNS: PATRICK "SPAZ" SPAZIANTE
PENCIL FINISHES: TRACY YARDLEY!
INKS: TERRY AUSTIN
COLORS: MATT HERMS
LETTERS: JOHN WORKMAN
SEE ANYTHING INTERESTING UP AHEAD?
OH, SURE!
WATER.
ROCKS.
MORE WATER.
CREEPY GARGOYLES.
DID I MENTION WATER?
COVER BY PATRICK SPAZIANTE • EDITOR: PAUL KAMINSKI
EDITOR-IN-CHIEF: VICTOR GORELICK • PRESIDENT: MIKE PELLERITO
SPECIAL THANKS TO CINDY CHAU AND JUDY GILBERTSON AT SEGA LICENSING
SONIC THE HEDGEHOG
SUPER-SPEEDY HERO
SALLY ACORN
COURAGEOUS LEADER
BOOMER WALRUS
MECHANIC
ANTOINE DEPARDIEU
EASILY STARTLED
CHECK OUT SONIC SUPER SPECIAL MAGAZINE #1 TO SEE HOW THIS ADVENTURE BEGAN!

OH, COME ON! IT FEELS COZY, IN ITS OWN WAY. KIND OF FAMILIAR. LIKE...
AN OLD LIMESTONE CAVERN?
YES! EXACTLY!
I WAS JUST THINKING THAT MYSELF.
OUI, MYSELF AS WELL. ARE YOU...
...ZE SIGH-KICK?
"SIGH-KICK"..?
THAT'S "PSYCHIC," 'TWAN.
OUI! ZE MIND-READERS!
WHICHEVER! VITE! WHAT DO YOU SEE IN MY BRAIN?
LOOKS COMPLETELY BLANK TO ME. SURPRISE-SURPRISE.
COME ON, GUYS. LET'S GET TO DR. EGGMAN'S BASE...
...BEFORE ANOTHER ONE OF THOSE EARTHQUAKES HIT.

THAT WAS PRETTY SLICK HOW YOU USED THAT ROBOT TO HELP US EARLIER.* WHERE DID YOU LEARN THAT STUFF?
AH, WELL. I DUNNO. IT JUST COMES NATURALLY TO ME.
*SUPER SPECIAL MAGAZINE #1
WELL, IT SURE CAME IN HANDY! YO, SAL, I'LL GIVE YOU A--
ALLOW ME, MA CHERIE!
THANKS, SWEETIE!
"MA CHERIE" ...?
"SWEETIE" ...?!

HEY, SAL? JUST HOW LONG HAVE YOU AND...
HOW LONG HAVE I WHAT? SONIC? HELLO?
...OOOKAY. C'MON, WE'LL DIVE TO THE NEXT PART OF THE--
DIVE?! INTO THE WATER?
UNLESS YOU PLAN TO DIVE INTO SOLID ROCK...?

NO WORRIES! RUINS LIKE THESE ARE FULL OF AIR POCKETS! WE'LL BE FINE!...
YEAH, BUT ...I CAN'T SWIM.
LIKE... AT ALL.
DON'T WORRY. YOU'LL DO JUST FINE WITH ME.
...SURE.
LEAD THE WAY.
OKAY... THIS ISN'T SO BAD...

GREAT. NOW WHAT?
OF COURSE...
...THERE WOULD BE ROBOTS DOWN HERE.
HERO TIME!
...IF I COULD, Y'KNOW, GET SOME SPEED GOING.
I HATE WATER.

AND NOW THAT I'VE GOT SPEED --THERE IS THIS!
IF I DODGE, I'LL LOSE ALL MY MOMENTUM.
UNLESS...

HRRRGH...!
ANTOINE ...!
REACH!
RUMBLE
EARTH-QUAKE!
ANTOINE!
WHOA!
SONIC!

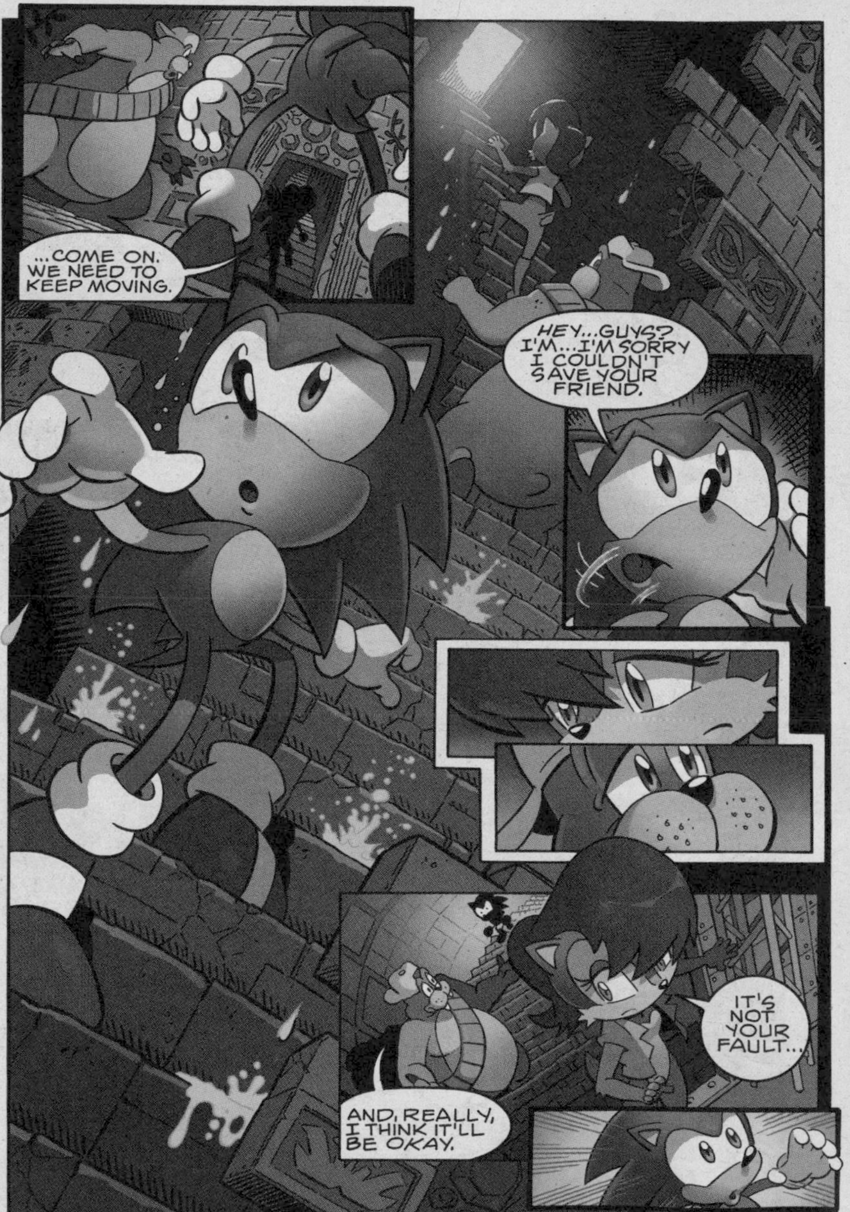
...COME ON. WE NEED TO KEEP MOVING.
HEY...GUYS? I'M...I'M SORRY I COULDN'T SAVE YOUR FRIEND.
IT'S NOT YOUR FAULT...
AND, REALLY, I THINK IT'LL BE OKAY.

OKAY, HOLD UP! YOUR BOYFRIEND JUST FALLS TO HIS DOOM, AND YOU'RE COOL WITH IT?!
FIRSTLY, ANTOINE ISN'T MY BOYFRIEND. WE WERE JUST *CLOSE* FRIENDS.
AND SECONDLY... IT DOESN'T FEEL RIGHT. I SAW HIM FALL, TOO, BUT... HE...
...HE CAN'T BE GONE.
THAT'S NOT *RIGHT.*
I FEEL IT, TOO. IT'S LIKE HOW THESE BADNIKS SEEM FAMILIAR, AND WE KEEP...
...SHARING THE SAME THOUGHTS?
RIGHT. IT'S *OKAY* BECAUSE WE *KNOW* IT WILL BE *OKAY.* MAYBE THAT'S JUST DENIAL, BUT...
NO, I GET WHAT YOU'RE SAYING.
I GUESS I CAN FEEL THAT, TOO.
C'MON, GUYS! THAT LITTLE DETOUR SET US BACK A BIT. LET'S TAKE THE FIGHT TO EGGMAN-- FOR ANTOINE!

WELL... HERE WE ARE. WELCOME TO THE SCENIC SCRAP BRAIN ZONE.
SERIOUSLY?
"SCRAP BRAIN"?
WHAT DOES THAT EVEN MEAN?
WHAT DO YOU WANT, SONIC? HE'S A MADMAN WHO PUTS ANIMALS INTO ROBOTS AND WANTS TO CONQUER THE WORLD.
AND LOOKS LIKE A TALKING EGG TO BOOT. NAH, THIS PLACE NEEDS A COOLER NAME, LIKE...LIKE... "ROBOTROPOLIS."
OOH-YEAH! OR-OR-OR... HOW ABOUT "NEW MEGA-OPOLIS"?
NAH, YOU'RE TRYING TOO HARD, BUDDY.
I GUESS. "ROBOTROPOLIS" DOES HAVE A RING TO IT.

IT'S TOO QUIET.
DOCTOR EGGMAN KNOWS WE'RE COMING. I WAS EXPECTING MORE...
...TRAPS?!
RRGH!
SONIC!
SALLY!

NO!
NOT AGAIN!
HRNH! WHEN THIS IS OVER...
...YOU'RE LAYING OFF JOE'S SUSHI!
I'LL GO ON AN EVERY-THING DIET! JUST DON'T DROP ME!
BOOMER, I'M SLIPPING! IS THERE ANY-THING...
...YOU CAN BRACE ON?
NOTHING! DROP ME AND SAVE YOUR-SELF!
NO, YOU'RE NOT PUTTING ME THROUGH THAT AGAIN!
PULL, MAN! PULL!

QUICK, PEOPLE! GET BELOW BEFORE ANYTHING ELSE HAPPENS!
YOU DO HAVE SOME KIND OF MAP OF THIS PLACE, RIGHT?
SORRY, SONIC. I'M FLYING BLIND HERE.
EVEN IF I DID, I DOUBT THIS PLACE WOULD MAKE ANY SENSE.
WOW. BET HE NEVER HAS TO LOOK FOR A CAN OPENER.
NOW...IF I WAS A MAD SCIENTIST IN HIDING, WHERE WOULD I--
--BE?

RIGHT HERE, YOU MISERABLE RODENT! YOU'VE DONE WELL TO GET THIS FAR.
THANKS...
...EGG-MAN.
I HAVE A REAL NAME, YOU KNOW!
I HATE THAT NICKNAME! WHY DOES EVERYONE CALL ME THAT?
LOOK, HOW ABOUT YOU SAVE US ALL A HEADACHE AND LET ME OUT OF THIS FORCE FIELD?
AH, BUT WHERE WOULD THE FUN BE IN THAT?
"FUN," HE SAYS...

AW, MAN-- DEAD END!
MARVELOUS CHOICE OF WORDS! FAREWELL, BOY.
CREEEAK
EH? THAT SOUNDS LIKE THE--
--HYDRAULICS PIPE.

ANTOINE?! YOU'RE OKAY!
NON! I AM NOT ZE OKAY!
I WASH AROUND IN ZE DARK FOR HOURS! I AM DIZZY AND SOGGY AND FRIGHTENED AND...
...BONJOUR.
EEEEEEEEEE EEEEEEEEEEEE EEEEEEEEEK!
THANKS FOR THE SAVE, 'TWAN!

NOW I'VE GOT YOU-- HEY!
STAY AWAY!
GOT IT!
GOOD WORK! SORRY TO MAKE YOU WAIT, SONIC...!
EH, YOU WERE HERE IN SPIRIT.
YOU'RE-- NOT--
--GETTING --AWAY-- THAT-- EASILY!
HE ESCAPED... HRRRRRGH!... DOWN HERE...
...AND SEALED IT SHUT!

HEY! GET BACK HERE, YOU COWARD!
EGAD!
WOW-- YOU'RE PRETTY FAST FOR A FAT MAN!
YOU'LL PAY FOR THIS, RODENT!
NOT LIKELY!
AAAARGH! I HATE THAT HEDGEHOG!!!
AUGH!

SONIC! WHAT HAPPENED TO EGGMAN?
HUMPTY-DUMPTY...
...HAD A GREAT FALL.
THEN IT'S OVER! WE DID IT!
THE WORLD IS SAFE!
OH, COME ON! YOU EARNED THIS AS MUCH AS THE REST OF US! MAYBE MORE!
...Y'KNOW HOW YOU WERE SO SURE ANTOINE WOULD BE OKAY?
YES...?
I'VE GOT THE SAME FEELING ABOUT EGGMAN.
THIS ISN'T OVER, SAL.
YOU'RE RIGHT, SONIC!
TURN THE PAGE FOR MORE AMAZING ADVENTURE IN THE WORLD OF SONIC GENESIS!
AND DON'T MISS OUT ON SONIC UNIVERSE, SONIC ARCHIVES, AND SONIC SELECTS!

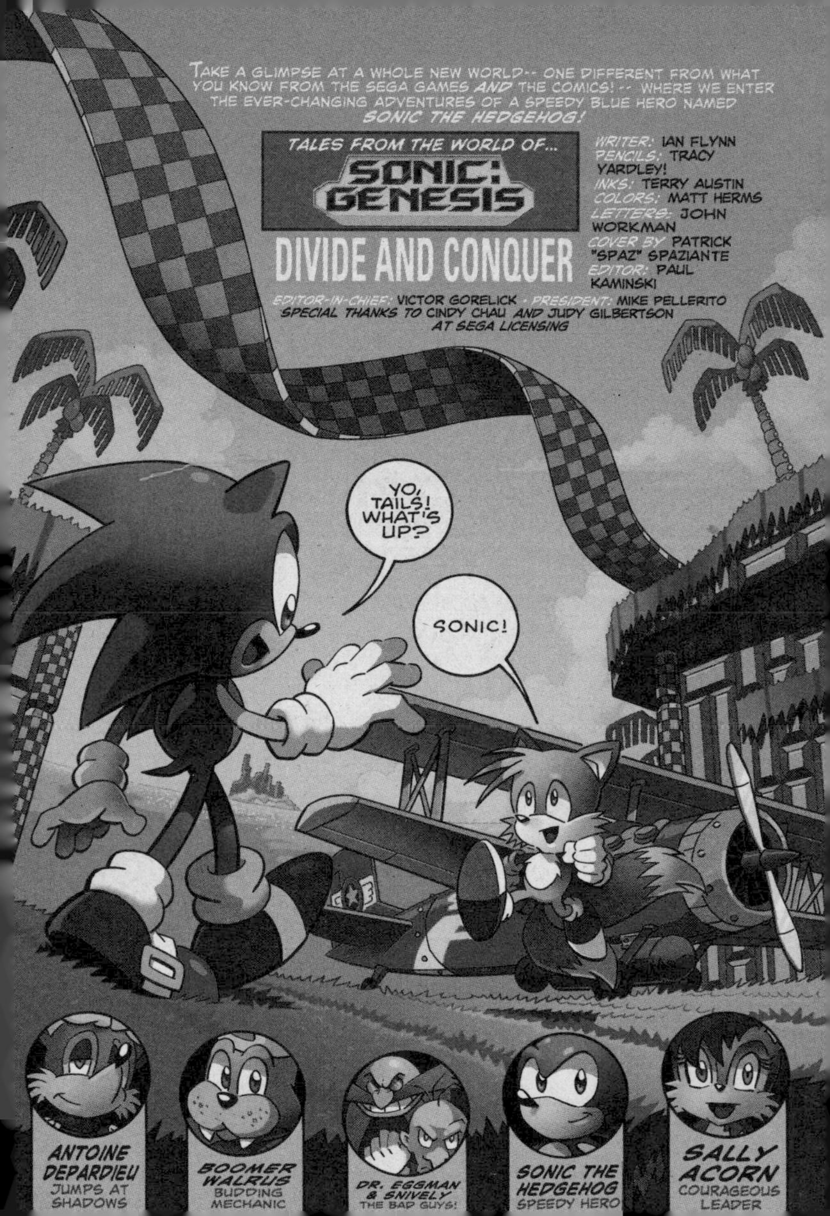

TAKE A GLIMPSE AT A WHOLE NEW WORLD-- ONE DIFFERENT FROM WHAT YOU KNOW FROM THE SEGA GAMES AND THE COMICS! -- WHERE WE ENTER THE EVER-CHANGING ADVENTURES OF A SPEEDY BLUE HERO NAMED SONIC THE HEDGEHOG!
TALES FROM THE WORLD OF...
SONIC: GENESIS
DIVIDE AND CONQUER
WRITER: IAN FLYNN
PENCILS: TRACY YARDLEY!
INKS: TERRY AUSTIN
COLORS: MATT HERMS
LETTERS: JOHN WORKMAN
COVER BY PATRICK "SPAZ" SPAZIANTE
EDITOR: PAUL KAMINSKI
EDITOR-IN-CHIEF: VICTOR GORELICK · PRESIDENT: MIKE PELLERITO
SPECIAL THANKS TO CINDY CHAU AND JUDY GILBERTSON AT SEGA LICENSING
YO, TAILS! WHAT'S UP?
SONIC!
ANTOINE DEPARDIEU JUMPS AT SHADOWS
BOOMER WALRUS BUDDING MECHANIC
DR. EGGMAN & SNIVELY THE BAD GUYS!
SONIC THE HEDGEHOG SPEEDY HERO
SALLY ACORN COURAGEOUS LEADER

WHO ARE YOUR FRIENDS?
THESE DUDES HELPED ME OUT ON MY LAST ADVENTURE. WAIT UNTIL YOU HEAR ABOUT IT!
GUYS, THIS IS WHO I WAS TELLING YOU ABOUT. MILES PROWER IS THE SMARTEST KID I KNOW.
HI THERE! MY NAME IS SALLY.
H-HI, YOU CAN CALL ME "TAILS."
BONJOUR.
YOU'VE GOT AN F 1 WITH A 9B NINE-CYLINDER ROTARY ENGINE!
YEAH! IT'S SONIC'S, BUT HE LETS ME TAKE CARE OF IT FOR HIM!
AND YOU SHOULD GET ALONG GREAT WITH... UH... BOOMER?!
WHERE DID HE GO?
OH, MAN!

WAITAMINUTE! YOU ADDED A HIGH-BYPASS TURBOFAN ENGINE?!
WELL, SONIC DOES PREFER TO GO FAST. AND IT WASN'T TOO HARD TO CONNECT THE FUEL LINES...
AND YOU'RE *HOW* OLD?!
TOTALLY CALLED IT. THEY'LL BE LIKE THIS FOR *HOURS.*
IT'S CUTE!
BESIDES, WE COULD ALL USE SOMETHING TO BE CHEERFUL ABOUT.
I SAW YOU WORKING ON THAT COMPUTER BEFORE WE LEFT THE SCRAP BRAIN ZONE. NOTHING BUT BAD NEWS?
PRETTY MUCH.
DOCTOR EGGMAN'S PRODUCTION PLANTS ARE STILL RUNNING, AND IT LOOKS LIKE YOU WERE RIGHT-- HE DID SURVIVE.
AND THERE WERE NO LEADS ABOUT ALL THE RECENT--
RRRRRRUMBLLE!

THAT WAS THE WORST TREMOR YET. IF EGG-MAN *IS* BEHIND THEM, WE NEED TO STOP HIM BEFORE THE ENTIRE PLANET SHAKES APART!
WHICH WOULD STINK, 'CAUSE THAT'S WHERE I KEEP ALL MY STUFF.
SO LET'S CUT TO THE CHASE, FIND THE DOC, AND BEAT THE UGLY OFF HIM, WHICH MIGHT TAKE A WEEK, BUT *HEY*...
NO...
WE NEED TO DISMANTLE HIS INFRASTRUC-TURE FIRST. HIS SUPPORT LINES MUST BE CUT!
BUT THAT PLAN SOUNDS SO *SLOW*...
ARE YOU GOING ON ANOTHER ADVENTURE, SONIC? CAN I COME, TOO?
I DON'T KNOW... YOU'RE AWFULLY YOUNG...
DON'T WORRY ABOUT TAILS. I TAUGHT HIM HOW TO HANDLE HIM-SELF.
ENOUGH WAITING! WE'LL FOLLOW YOUR PLAN FOR NOW, SAL. YOU'VE GOT THE DIREC-TIONS TO EGG-MAN'S NEXT FACTORY?
I SURE DO! HE WON'T KNOW WHAT HIT HIM!

MEANWHILE...
WAHA-HA-HA! WITH PHASE ONE WELL BEHIND US, THIS GLORIOUS FLYING FORTRESS CAN MOVE ON TO PHASE TWO OF MY BRILLIANT PLAN!
ABOUT THAT, SIR. WHAT WAS PHASE ONE?
IT WAS BRILLIANT! WE DID THAT... THING...TO THE PLANET!
YOU KNOW...THAT THING...IT PRIMED MOBIUS FOR... PHASE TWO.
BAH! IT DOESN'T MATTER WHETHER YOU REMEMBER IT OR NOT!
WHATEVER IT WAS, IT SEVERELY DRAINED THE POWER RESERVES!

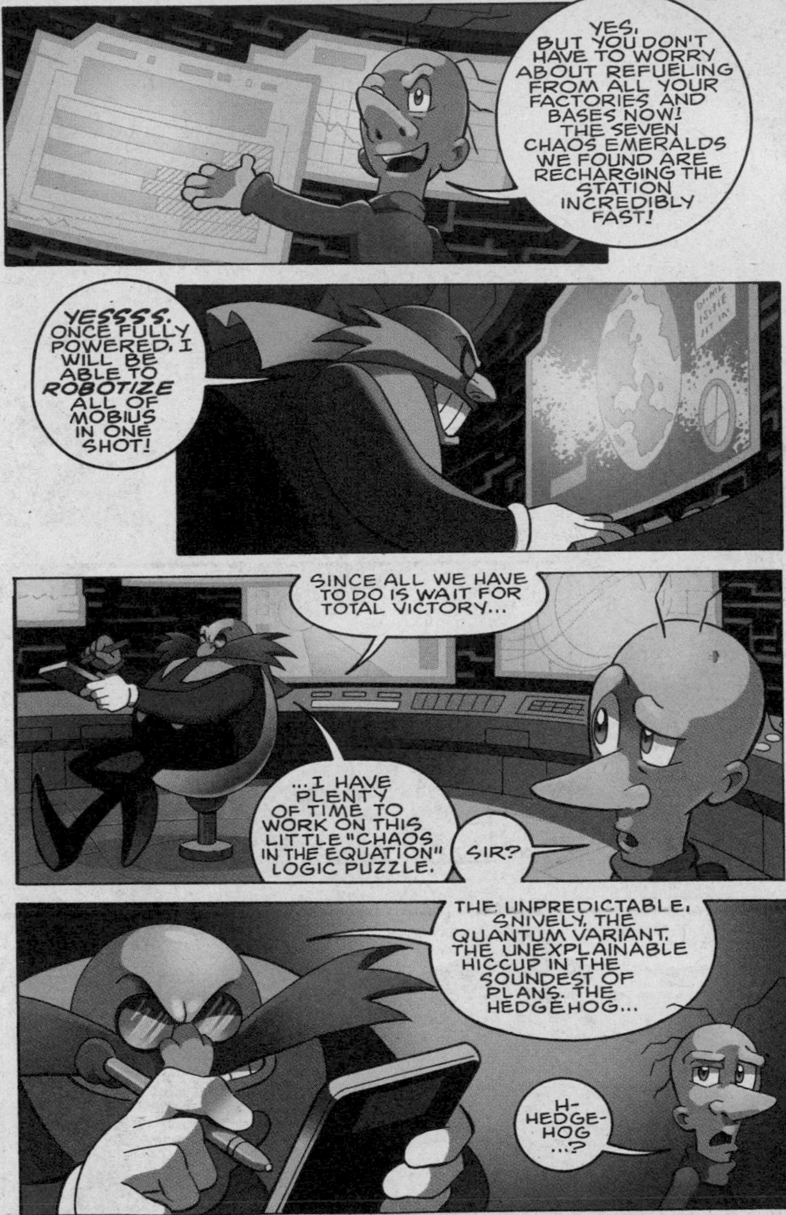
YES, BUT YOU DON'T HAVE TO WORRY ABOUT REFUELING FROM ALL YOUR FACTORIES AND BASES NOW! THE SEVEN CHAOS EMERALDS WE FOUND ARE RECHARGING THE STATION INCREDIBLY FAST!
YESSSS. ONCE FULLY POWERED, I WILL BE ABLE TO ROBOTIZE ALL OF MOBIUS IN ONE SHOT!
SINCE ALL WE HAVE TO DO IS WAIT FOR TOTAL VICTORY...
...I HAVE PLENTY OF TIME TO WORK ON THIS LITTLE "CHAOS IN THE EQUATION" LOGIC PUZZLE.
SIR?
THE UNPREDICTABLE, SNIVELY. THE QUANTUM VARIANT. THE UNEXPLAINABLE HICCUP IN THE SOUNDEST OF PLANS. THE HEDGEHOG...
H-HEDGE-HOG...?

ERM... SHOULDN'T WE BE PAY-ING SOME ATTENTION TO THE DIMENSIONAL DISTURBANCES? THEY'VE CAUSED HEAVY SEISMIC ACTIVITY RECENTLY...
...BUT PRELIMINARY READINGS SUGGEST A TOTAL SPACE-TIME COLLAPSE. IT'S LIKE REALITY HAS BEEN STRETCHED AND IS FIGHTING TO SNAP BACK.
HMM?
WHAT-EVER. I'LL HAVE WON BEFORE THEN.
LET ME WORK.
WHAT ABOUT THE REBEL MOBIANS WHO ATTACKED US? THEY'RE SURE TO TRY TO CAUSE MORE PROBLEMS!
OH, DON'T WORRY ABOUT THEM, SNIVELY.
I MADE SURE MY FACILITIES ARE READY...
...FOR UNINVITED GUESTS.

HERE WE ARE, FOLKS, THE CHEMICAL PLANT ZONE.
SOMEHOW I DON'T THINK THIS PLACE MEETS OCCUPATIONAL HAZARD GUIDELINES.
WHICH MEANS IT WILL BE A LOT OF FUN TO RUN AROUND IN!
IS HE POLLUTING FOR POLLUTION'S SAKE? WHY WOULD HE NEED TO PRODUCE THIS MUCH CHEMICAL FUEL?
UNLESS HE'S STOCKPILING IT ALL...
OR IF IT'S MEANT FOR A TRULY MONSTROUS MACHINE!
CAN YOU IMAGINE HOW MANY JOULES THAT MUCH FUEL COULD PRODUCE?!
CAN YOU IMAGINE A DEVICE THAT NEEDED THAT KIND OF POWER?!
ARE WE TRYING TO STOP ZE MADMAN'S SCHEMES, OR ARE WE PUTTING TOGETHER ZE FANNING CLUB FOR HIM?
DON'T BE SUCH A SPOILSPORT, ANTOINE. C'MON, LET'S SEE ABOUT SHUTTING THIS PLACE DOWN.

WOW. THIS PLACE IS DECEPTIVELY HUGE!
I WAS KNOWING IT! WE ARE TRAPPED IN HERE FOREVER!
GIVE IT A REST, 'TWAN. WE CAN FIND OUR WAY OUT EASILY.
THE REAL PROBLEM IS FINDING THE WAY WE *WANT* TO GO.
ALL THESE PIPES HAVE TO GO **SOMEWHERE**, RIGHT? I'LL JUST SPEED THROUGH THEM AND FIND WHERE WE NEED TO GO!
I'M SURE I CAN FIGURE OUT WHICH PIPE WE NEED TO FOLLOW, AND...
YEAH-YEAH-YEAH! **RACE YA!**
HA HA HA! YOU'RE CRAZY!

ZWEEE!
ZWEEE!
ZWEEE!
AH-HA!

WE NEED TO GO THIS WAY!
CHEATER! YOU FOLLOWED ME UP HERE!
HA HA! NO, I DIDN'T!
Y'KNOW...
...YOU COULD'VE WAITED ANOTHER MINUTE, GONE AROUND THE BEND WITH US AND FOUND THIS ELEVATOR.
YEAH ...BUT WHERE WOULD THE FUN BE IN THAT?

SOON...
THIS LOOKS LIKE A SUPPLY DELIVERY ROUTE...
COOL, WE'LL JUST HOP ONE OF THESE CRATES AND RIDE OUR WAY TO THE TOP!
THEY LOOK PRETTY HEAVY. WHATEVER IS PULLING THEM UP SHOULD BE ENOUGH TO CARRY OUR WEIGHT, TOO!
I DON'T KNOW. THIS ALL SEEMS TOO CONVENIENT.
YOU GUYS WORRY TOO MUCH. WOO-HA!
MUST WE BE ZE LEAPING WIZOUT ZE LOOKING? LAST TIME MOI WAS NEARLY DROWN-ED.
YOU MADE IT OUT OKAY. YOU EVEN SAVED SONIC!
WAIT FOR ME! WHEEEEE!
THE REAL PROBLEM IN THE LABYRINTH ZONE WAS THE--
EARTHQUAKE!

CLANG!
THIS PLACE IS FILLING WITH MEGA MUCK!
I KNEW IT WOULD BE A TRAP!
SHOOMP!
GLOOP!
MEGA-WHAT?
MEGA MUCK! A VISCOUS POLYMER WITH TOXIC PROPERTIES!
...MEANING?
WE'RE GOING TO DROWN IN POISON SOUP!
AH.

START FLYING THEM UP. I'LL MAKE US A WAY OUT.
O-OKAY!
ANTOINE, GO! WE'LL START CLIMBING!
SALLY! COME ON!
WHAM
DOOR'S OPEN AT THE TOP!
RRRGH-- THANKS!
GO ON AHEAD! I'LL SWIM TO THE TOP!
I'M NOT LEAVING YOU BEHIND!
SOME-BODY CALL FOR A--

WHOA!
--RESCUE?
I WAS COMING BACK FOR YOU, Y'KNOW?
I THOUGHT I'D SAVE YOU THE TRIP...!
I COULD CLIMB OUT ON MY OWN...
WHERE WOULD THE FUN BE IN THAT?
WHERE INDEED?
ARE YOU OKAY? ALL "HEROED" OUT?
PANT I'M FINE. WHEW I JUST CAN'T FLY TOO LONG...

THAT TEARS IT. WE SHUT THIS PLACE DOWN, THEN FIND EGGMAN AND TEACH HIM TO TRY AND TRAP US!
LET'S NOT GET AHEAD OF OUR-SELVES...
DID THE FUMES GO TO YOUR HEAD?
I WANT TO END THIS QUICKLY, TOO, BUT IT'S LIKE I SAID EARLIER. WE HAVE TO CUT HIS SUPPORT LINES, OR WE'RE GOING TO BE DEALING WITH HIM OVER AND OVER AGAIN.
IF WE RUSH IN, SOMEBODY'S GOING TO GET HURT.
NOBODY'S GOING TO GET HURT AS LONG AS I'M--
SONIC...?
FINE, HAVE IT YOUR WAY. YOU GO TO THE BASES. I'M HEADING FOR THE BIG MAN.

SO THAT'S IT? YOU'RE JUST WALKING OUT ON US?!
I DON'T WALK. I RUN. IT'S BEEN FUN, GUYS. LATER.
UM ...I'M GOING WITH SONIC. IT WAS NICE MEETING YOU, THOUGH!
LIKE-WISE.
ANTOINE AND I WILL STICK WITH YOU, SALLY. YOU HAVEN'T LED US ASTRAY.
I AM CONFUS-ED. WERE WE JUST DUMPED?
LET'S SHUT THIS PLACE DOWN, GUYS.
SMOOTH, 'TWAN.
WHAT? THAT IS WHAT YOU ARE CALLING IT WHEN SOMEONE WALKS OUT ON YOU, NON?

LATER-- OIL OCEAN ZONE.
NOT TOO MUCH FURTHER, BOYS. WE SHUT THIS PLACE DOWN, AND DR. EGGMAN LOSES OVER HALF OF HIS ENERGY RESOURCES.
SAL, I'M SORRY IF THIS IS A SORE TOPIC, BUT SHOULDN'T WE HAVE MADE AN EFFORT TO KEEP SONIC AROUND?
NOT TO BELITTLE OUR EFFORTS, BUT WE COULD REALLY USE HIS SKILLS ABOUT NOW.
NO, BOOMER. YOU'RE RIGHT. I WASN'T ...I WASN'T THINKING BACK THERE...

RRRRRRRRRRRRUMBLE!!!
FIRST ZE SMELL OF ZIS PLACE -URP- AND THEN ZE TREMORS...
MOBIUS IS SHAKING ITSELF APART.
THEN WE NEED TO SHUT DOWN EGGMAN'S PLANS AS FAST AS POSSIBLE.

MEANWHILE-- METROPOLIS ZONE...
WE'RE COMING UP ON DR. EGGMAN'S CITY, SONIC! IT WOULD BE NICE IF WE HAD SOME BACK-UP, DON'T YOU THINK?
NAH. IT'S BETTER THIS WAY.
THEY CAN HANDLE THEM-SELVES.
I MEANT MORE ABOUT US. WE'RE IN WAY OVER OUR HEADS...
DON'T SWEAT IT, LITTLE BRO'! YOU JUST KEEP THE TORNADO SAFE WHILE I RUIN EGGMAN'S DAY! THEN WE'LL FLY OFF TO OUR HAPPILY-EVER-AFTER.
IF YOU SAY SO...
I'LL HAVE MY RADIO ON SO WE CAN KEEP IN TOUCH. SEE YOU IN A BIT!

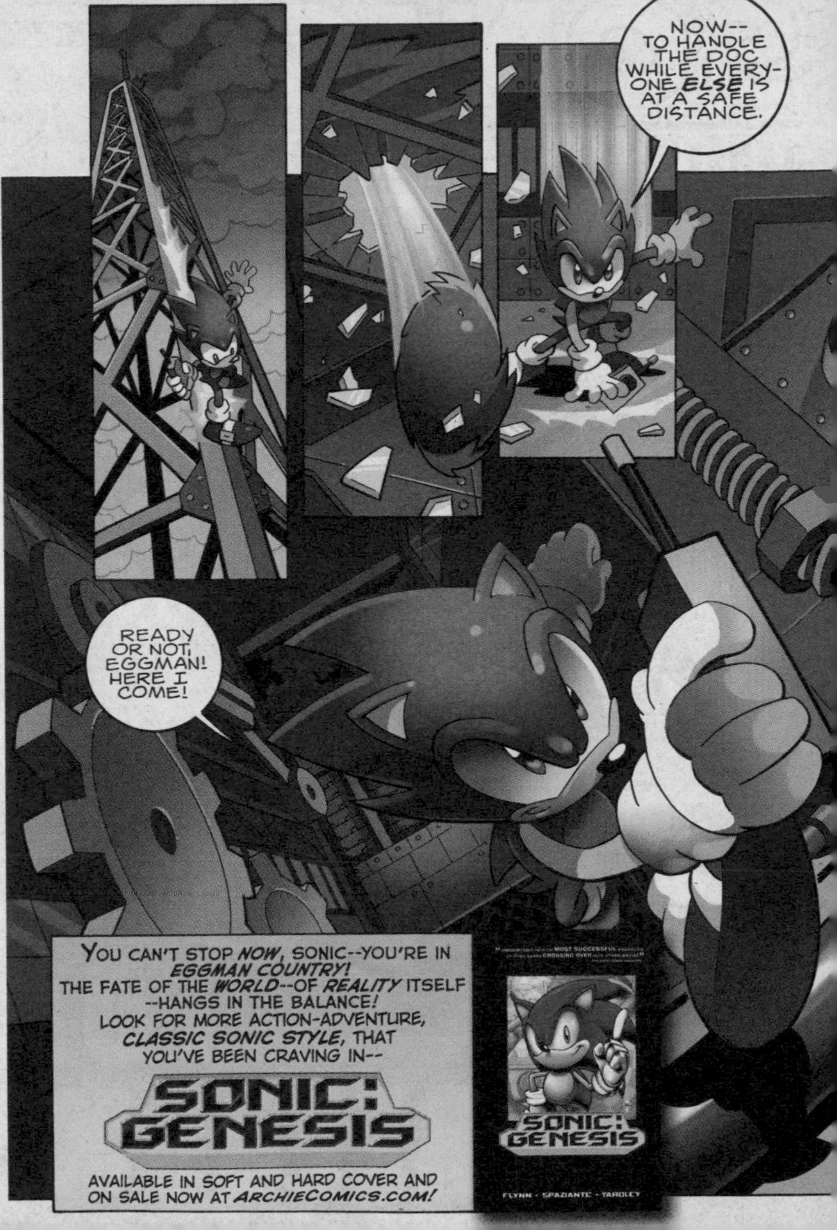

NOW-- TO HANDLE THE DOC WHILE EVERYONE ELSE IS AT A SAFE DISTANCE.
READY OR NOT, EGGMAN! HERE I COME!
YOU CAN'T STOP NOW, SONIC--YOU'RE IN EGGMAN COUNTRY!
THE FATE OF THE WORLD--OF REALITY ITSELF --HANGS IN THE BALANCE!
LOOK FOR MORE ACTION-ADVENTURE, CLASSIC SONIC STYLE, THAT YOU'VE BEEN CRAVING IN--
SONIC: GENESIS
AVAILABLE IN SOFT AND HARD COVER AND ON SALE NOW AT ARCHIECOMICS.COM!
SONIC: GENESIS
FLYNN · SPAZIANTE · YARDLEY

SONIC THE HEDGEHOG
SONIC SUPER DIGEST
PIN-UP PAGE!
SAYS....
FIGHT FOR FREEDOM!

TIME & AGAIN
PRISON ISLAND-- WHITE JUNGLE ONE YEAR AGO
I FOUND YOU, FAKER!
FAKER? I THINK YOU'RE THE FAKE HEDGEHOG AROUND HERE.

Writer: IAN FLYNN ○ Pencils: TRACY YARDLEY! ○ Inks: JIM AMASH ○ Colors: JASON JENSEN
Letters: TERESA DAVIDSON

Editor/Managing Editor: MIKE PELLERITO ○ Editor-in-Chief: VICTOR GORELICK

Special thanks to KRISTIN PARCELL & CINDY CHAU at Sega Licensing

YOU'RE COMPARING YOURSELF TO ME?
YOU'RE NOT GOOD ENOUGH TO BE MY FAKE.
I'LL MAKE YOU EAT THOSE WORDS!
THIS IS ROUGE. I'M IN THE VAULTS. THOSE EXTRA SIX EMERALDS ARE AS GOOD AS OURS!

TONK! TONK!
HZZZMAH...?
WAKE UP, BLUE HEDGEHOG. WE NEED TO TALK.
NEW MEGAOPOLIS-- OUTSIDE THE EGGDOME PRESENT DAY
SONIC THE HEDGEHOG HERO OF MOBIUS
YAWN!
SHADOW THE HEDGEHOG LIVING WEAPON

EVENING, FAKER.
COME TO JOIN THE INVASION?
OTHER WAY AROUND, ACTUALLY.
ROUGE AND I ARE ON A SUPPORT MISSION. I THOUGHT YOU'D WANT IN.
SOUNDS COOL. LET ME WAKE UP THE OTHERS AND WE'LL GO.
NO. IT'S A SMALL, SURGICAL STRIKE. THIS IS SIMPLY A COURTESY CALL.
BY EXCLUSIVE INVITATION ONLY, huh?
I CAN WORK WITH THAT.
BE RIGHT WITH YA!
THOOMP

ALRIGHT! SO WHERE'S THE PARTY?
ROUGE IS WAITING AT THE RENDEZVOUS POINT THREE CLICKS TO NORTHEAST. IT'S A LARGE CONVERTED OBSERVATORY.
COOL, RACE YA!
Hmph!

ONE YEAR AGO
THIS IS ROBOTNIK! I'VE SET THE CHARGES! THE ISLAND WILL BLOW IN FIVE MINUTES!
WAIT-- EXPLODE?!
THAT'S... A PROBLEM. ROUGE HERE. THE VAULT'S GONE INTO LOCK-DOWN AND I'M... WELL...
BAH! SHADOW, RENDEZVOUS WITH ME. WE'LL DIG THE EMERALDS OUT OF THE ASHES.
NOT COOL! LOOK, I'LL HELP YOU RESCUE YOUR FRIEND. TRUCE FOR NOW?
FOR NOW.

05:00
04:00
03:00
02:00
01:00
MY HERO.
CHAOS--!
QUICK, WHICH WAY IS--

THAT WAS SO UNLIKE YOU, SHADOW. TO COME AND RESCUE--
I WAS ONLY AFTER THE CHAOS EMERALDS.
CHAOS...
FWASH
--CONTROL!
--THE EXIT?
...CONTROL!
FWASH
HEY!
SONIC THE HEDGEHOG.
I KNOW. ROUGE THE BAT.
ENCHANTED. I THINK WE SHOULD COMPLAIN TO THAT GUY'S MANAGER.
I CONCUR.
AND I KNOW JUST HOW TO GET TO THE MAN IN CHARGE.

PRESENT
LEAVE IT TO THE DOC TO TURN A TELESCOPE INTO A KILLER-RAY-SHOOTER-THING.
A HIGH-GRADE ONE AT THAT.
ROUGE THE BAT SUPER SPY
AS BEST AS I CAN TELL, THIS THING WILL VAPORIZE YOUR FORCE FIELD, YOUR CAMP, AND HALF OF THE EGGDOME ITSELF.
YOU SURE? THAT SEEMS A BIT OVER THE TOP, EVEN FOR ROBOTNIK.
NOT ANYMORE.

WE BELIEVE THE DOCTOR IS LOSING HIS LAST HOLD ON REALITY. THIS IS BUT ONE MORE PIECE OF EVIDENCE.
NICE OF YOU TO SHOW UP. GET LOST?
YOU HAD A HEAD START.
AND I THINK YOU'RE OFF, FAKER. EGGMAN'S A FEW CHIPS SHY OF A MOTHERBOARD, BUT HE'S NOT THAT FAR GONE.
BELIEVE WHAT YOU WANT. JUST DON'T UNDERESTIMATE HIM WHEN YOUR TIME COMES.
LET'S PSYCHOANALYZE THE DOCTOR LATER AND TAKE CARE OF THE DOOM LASER FIRST, *hmm?*
THE LADY HAS A POINT.
COVER ME WHILE I HACK THE SYSTEM, BOYS!
CRASH

ZZT!
ZZZT!
THE CANNON'S MOVING INTO POSITION, ROUGE.
WORKING ON IT. KEEP THE LASERS OFF ME.
WAY TOO EASY!

PRESENT
POW
YOW!
THAT CANNON'S MOVING ALONG PRETTY QUICK, ROUGE!
ONE YEAR AGO
ZAP
HOW ARE YOU COMING WITH THAT KEY, ROUGE?
PRESENT
GAH!
I TRIGGERED SOME KIND OF SELF-DESTRUCT ON THE CONSOLE!
I CAN'T STOP THE CANNON!

ONE YEAR AGO
YOU DO KNOW HOW TO FLY THIS THING, RIGHT?
STRAP IN AND HOLD ON, AND WE'LL FIND OUT!
BWOOM
PRESENT
YOU'RE SURE WE CAN'T STOP IT?
NOT QUIETLY OR CLEANLY.
THEN WE DO NEITHER.

CHAOS SPEAR!
NO GOOD!
WHAM
WHAT'S THIS THING MADE OF?!
WE MIGHT HAVE A CHANCE IF YOU CAN BREAK THE COUPLING LOCKS!
IF YOU BREAK WHERE IT ALL JOINS TOGETHER, WE CAN MAYBE THROW OFF THE ANGLE OF THE SHOT!

ONE YEAR AGO
OUT OF THE WAY, FAKER! I'M NOT LETTING THAT ECLIPSE CANNON FIRE!
I PROMISED THE WORLD REVENGE!
I WILL NOT BE DENIED!
HATE TO DISAPPOINT, BUT THERE'S A FEW BILLION FOLKS DOWN THERE WHO WILL THANK ME LATER!
CHAOS...
...SPEAR!
AUGH!
SHADOW, STOP! IT'S ROUGE. I'VE GOT A VIDEO HERE I THINK YOU SHOULD SEE...

PRESENT
I'VE GOT THE LEFT LOCK-THINGIE!
I'LL TAKE RIGHT.
CREEEAK
CRASH!
NO!
WE JUST PUT IT AT THE ANGLE TO FIRE!

ONE YEAR AGO
GYAAAAAH!
FWASH
WAS THAT...
...CHAOS CONTROL?!
THE BEAST HAS FUSED WITH THE ARK! IT'S PULLING US TOWARDS MOBIUS!
MARIA... I FAILED YOU.
NOT SO FAST, FAKER. WE'VE GOT SEVEN TRUMP CARDS RIGHT HERE.

ONE YEAR AGO
HEY, UGLY! THAT'S MY PLANET! NO TOUCHIE!
PRESENT
I'M TAKING OFF MY INHIBITOR RINGS. HOPEFULLY THAT'LL GIVE ME ENOUGH POWER TO DIVERT THE LASER.
GOOD LUCK, SHADOW.

CHAOS--
--CONTROL!!!
TIME TO PUT THE ARK BACK INTO ORBIT!
NOW, SONIC!
CHAOS CONTROL!!!

SHADOW!
THIS IS WHAT YOU WANTED...
...WASN'T IT...
...MARIA?
WHA--?
YEAH, WE'RE NOT GOING THROUGH THAT AGAIN.

AND SO...
WELL, BETWEEN THE OVER-POWERED SHOT AND SHADOW'S TECHNIQUE, THE THING IS OFFICIALLY BEYOND REPAIR.
DOESN'T THAT JUST BREAK YOUR HEART.
GET SOME REST, BLUE HEDGEHOG. YOU HAVE A BIG FIGHT AHEAD OF YOU TOMORROW.
NOT PLANNING ON STEALING MY SPOTLIGHT, FAKER?
NO.
I OWE YOU MUCH. THE LEAST I CAN DO IS STAND ASIDE AND LET YOU FINISH THINGS WITH THE DOCTOR. THIS IS *YOUR* FIGHT.
WOW. I APPRECIATE THAT, SHADOW.
GOOD LUCK, SONIC.

MY-MY-MY!
WHAT?
LOOK HOW FAR YOUR RELATIONSHIP HAS COME!
Hmph.
HE HAS MY RESPECT, THAT'S ALL.
OF COURSE. FAR TOO SCANDALOUS FOR YOU TWO TO BE FRIENDS.
THE SHADOW SAGA CONTINUES WITH MORE TEAM DARK ACTION IN VOL. 1 OF THE--
SONIC UNIVERSE™
GRAPHIC NOVEL SERIES! AND DON'T FORGET SONIC SUPER SPECIAL MAGAZINE, SONIC ARCHIVES, AND SONIC SELECTS ALSO AVAILABLE AT ARCHIECOMICS.COM!
SONIC UNIVERSE
THE SHADOW SAGA
FLYNN · YARDLEY

SONIC SUPER DIGEST
PIN-UP PAGE!

...SO YOU CAN SEE WHY MY FATHER APPROVED THE METAL SONIC TROOPERS.*
YEAH, I'LL BUY IT. BUT YOUR OLD MAN SHOUD'VE KNOWN THAT A LITTLE DOOMSDAY WEAPON CAN'T STOP ME.**
*SEE SONIC #159
**SEE STH #125
DULY NOTED.
CAN YOU PROMISE ME THAT'S THE LAST "BRILLIANT IDEA" YOU ROYALS COME UP WITH?
SALLY AND I HAVE JUST ONE MORE LEFT.
OH, YEAH?
YOU'RE NOT NIXING THE GREAT OAK SLIDE, ARE YOU?
THE EXACT OPPOSITE, SONIC.

BIRTHDAY BASH!
Part One: GIVING AND RECEIVING
Writer: IAN FLYNN
Pencils: TRACY YARDLEY!
Inks: JIM AMASH
Letters: JOHN WORKMAN
Colors: JASON JENSEN
Cover: PAT "SPAZ" SPAZIANTE
Editor: MIKE PELLERITO
Managing Editor: VICTOR GORELICK
Editor-in-Chief: Richard Goldwater
HAPPY BIRTHDAY SONIC
HAPPY BIRTHDAY!
HAPPY BIRTHDAY, HANDSOME!
YOU GUYS FIXED UP THE OLD BASE!*
*WAY, WAY BACK IN SONIC ARCHIVES, VOL. 1!
...AND A STEP BACK TO SIMPLER TIMES. HAPPY BIRTHDAY, SONIC.
A PLACE FOR THE FREEDOM FIGHTERS TO PLAN, A NEW FOCAL POINT FOR DOCTOR ROBOTNIK THAT IS AWAY FROM OUR FAMILIES...
THANKS, SAL.
SO, BLUE... HOW OLD ARE YOU NOW?
WELL, IF WE TAKE HIS TRIP INTO SPACE INTO ACCOUNT... **
LET'S CALL ME A TEEN FROM NOW TIL FOREVER.
**SEE STH#126
KA BOOM

HAPPY BIRTHDAY, SONIC! YOU CAN THANK ROBOTNIK! HE HIRED US TO BLAST YOU! SOMETHING THAT ENDS IN -ICK!
HERE COME YOUR BIRTHDAY SPANKINGS!
AAW! EGGMAN SHOULDN'T HAVE! IT'S SWEET THAT HE RE-MEMBERED, THO'!
WITH NACK IN JAIL*, I GUESS HE HAD TO SHOP FOR NEW THUGS. YOU LOOK LIKE QUITE THE FIGHTER!
AND ONE FOR YOU! AND ONE FOR YOU! AND ONE FOR YOU!
BAM!
*SEE STH #154.
HEY!
CRACK!
WHUD
DON'T TRASH THE GREAT OAK SL--
OOF!

GOTCHA, SONIC!
THANKS, LITTLE BRO'. I THINK I KNOW WHY THESE GUYS TOOK THE JOB.
EVIL SONIC DID A LOT OF STUFF UNDER MY NAME.* I'VE MANAGED TO GET THE GIRLS TO UNDERSTAND, BUT...
*SEE STH# 150-151
TIME-OUT, BUDDY!
I THINK THERE'S BEEN A MISTAKE. THERE'S A JERK WHO LOOKS LIKE ME WHO CAUSED SOME TROUBLE A BIT BACK, AND...
NO MISTAKE THERE, MISTER NEEDLEMOUSE! SO YOU GOT AN EVIL TWIN?

"FRANKLY, COBALT, I DON'T GIVE A DARN!"
NOW THIS IS MORE LIKE IT!
LET THE MASTER THIEF STEAL THE GEM AND LEAVE THE DECOY DUTIES TO--
--EVIL SONIC?!
...OH, SNAP. LOCKE DIDN'T CATCH YOU?
THE DEAL WAS...YOU DISTRACT HIM THIS TIME!
I DIDN'T SEE HIM, SO I FIGURED HE'D GOTTEN TO YOU ALREADY!
AHEM.
MY PATIENCE HAS WORN THIN.
GIVE ME A BREAK, MAN!

KONK KONK KONK
"IT'S MY BIRTHDAY!"
I HOPE THIS STILL WORKS...
HEY, BEAN! SEE THE SHINIES? YOU WANT THE SHINY KEYS?
SHINY?!
GO GET 'EM!
SHINIES!!!
NICE MOVE, FIONA, BUT... HOW DO YOU KNOW...?
ER... HOLD THAT THOUGHT, SONIC.
YOU'RE OUT-NUMBERED, BARK. YOU CAN'T TAKE ALL OF US AT ONCE.

I'M GLAD YOU'RE STILL REASONABLE.
WHY, THANK YOU, MISS SHINY-KEYS! I THINK YOUR ACCENT IS ADORABLE! I'VE HAD FUN, BUT I NEED TO GET BACK TO WORK! OF COURSE YOU CAN HAVE MY NUMBER!
HEY! LOOK! SHINE GET! WANNA COME PUMMEL SONIC? IT'S GOOD FOR YOUR GLUTES.

YOU HAVE A LOT OF EXPLAINING TO DO, FIONA!
SORRY FOR HELPING OUT. GO, TEAM.
THAT'S NOT THE POINT. HOW DO YOU KNOW THESE TWO?
LOOK, I... I'VE HAD A CHECKERED PAST, OKAY?
I HAVEN'T ALWAYS BEEN A FREEDOM FIGHTER.
BUT YOU'RE A WELCOME PART OF THE TEAM, FI. SHOULDN'T WE GO LOOKING FOR BEAN?
NO NEED.
HAPPY BIRTHDAY, BLUE HEDGEHOG. I CLEANED YOUR YARD FOR YOU.

WE HAVE TO STOP MEETING LIKE THIS, LOCKE.
HIT HIM BEFORE HE USES HIS WACKY VOODOO!
WHOA!
GAH! TOLJA!
FIRST RULE OF A GUARDIAN: DEAL WITH THE LARGEST THREAT FIRST.
FLATTERY WILL GET YOU NOWHERE, OLD MAN.
EVIL SONIC! GIVE ME A HAND!
SORRY, ROUGE, BUT THE BIRTHDAY BOY GETS DIBS ON THE GOODS!
YOU JERK!

WOO-HAH! HAPPY BIRTHDAY TO ME!
LOOKS LIKE YOUR PRIORITIES JUST SHIFTED. SERVES YOU RIGHT, TRAITOR.
NO!!!
GET OFF OF THE MASTER EMERALD!
YOU BOTH HAD YOUR CHANCE.
YOU LIKE TO PLAY IT ROUGH, HUH? LET'S GO!
THE BIRTHDAY BOY GETS FIRST DIBS, ROUGE.

SO, WHAT'S THE OCCASION, FAKER? AS YOU CAN SEE, MY DANCE CARD IS FULL.
I DID NOT COME TO FIGHT, BLUE HEDGEHOG. I CAME TO THANK YOU.
THANK ME?
WITHOUT YOU, THE METAL SONIC TROOPS WOULD'VE KILLED HOPE.* YOU WERE THERE FOR HER WHEN I SHOULD HAVE BEEN. SO...THANK YOU.
*SEE SONIC 159
NOW THAT THIS CHANGES NOTHING. FOR THE MOMENT, I WORK WITH DOCTOR ROBOTNIK, AND WE ARE ENEMIES.
IT'D BE BORING OTHER-WISE. FEEL FREE TO GET A CLUE AND QUIT EGGMAN ANY TIME, THOUGH.
WORRIED?
YOU WISH, FAKER.
HAS ANYBODY SEEN BEAN LATELY?
HE'S IN THE BRAIN TRUST'S ROOM...AND HE HAS DR. ROBOTNIK ON THE LINE!

...AND SO, YEAH, WE GOT BEAT. JUST THOUGHT I'D LET YOU KNOW.
NEVER TRUST A MOBIAN TO DO A ROBOT'S JOB. YOU'RE FIRED. I'M SENDING ONE OF MY OWN TO FINISH THE JOB!
BEAN? GO SIT WITH BARK.
AWW...
WHAT ARE YOU SENDING NOW, EGGMAN? YOUR NEWEST TOYS BROKE EASILY.
I'M LAUNCHING IT NOW, SONIC. HAPPY BIRTHDAY! MWAHAHAHA HA!
LAUNCH? INCOMING MISSILE?
NO, SOME KIND OF ONE-WAY TRANSPORT...
WHUD
THAT WAS FAST.

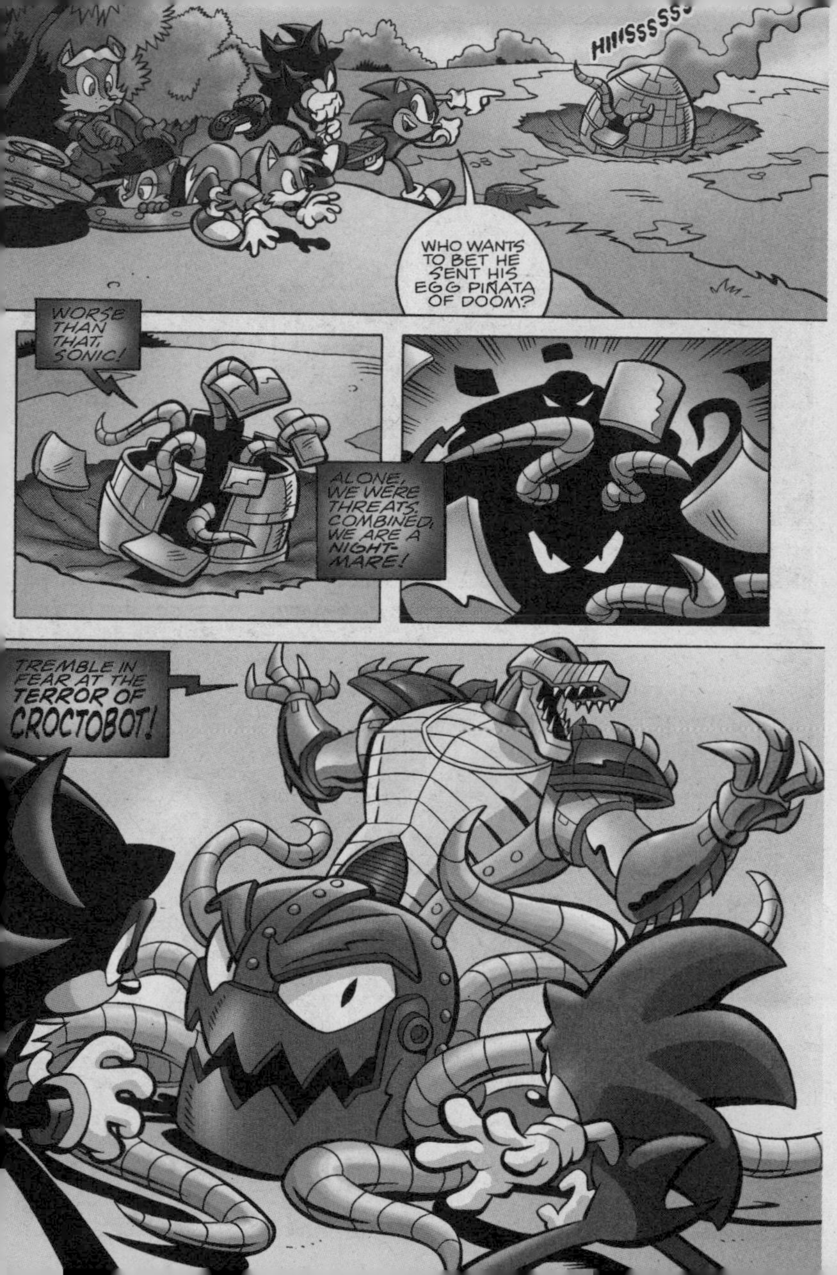
HIIISSSSSS
WHO WANTS TO BET HE SENT HIS EGG PIÑATA OF DOOM?
WORSE THAN THAT, SONIC!
ALONE, WE WERE THREATS. COMBINED, WE ARE A NIGHT-MARE!
TREMBLE IN FEAR AT THE TERROR OF CROCTOBOT!

EVIL SONIC... ?
NOT QUITE, BABE.
BUT A REAL SCOURGE ALL THE SAME.
TO BE CONTINUED!

SONIC SUPER DIGEST
PIN-UP PAGE!

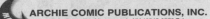

TODAY'S MY BIRTHDAY!
TODAY'S MY BIRTHDAY.
DOCTOR ROBOTNIK SENT A PAIR OF ASSASSINS AS A PRESENT. THE GUY'S ALL CLASS.
I GOT A POWER-BOOST OFF THE MASTER EMERALD. A HECKUVA GIFT.
NOW I'M FACING OFF AGAINST SOME SUPER-BADNIK.
NOW I'VE BEEN TRANS-FORMED INTO A REAL TOUGH GUY.
OH, AND SHADOW'S HERE.
OH, AND ROUGE IS HERE.

BIRTHDAY BASH!

Part Two: BIRTHDAY BOYS

Writer: IAN FLYNN
Penciler: TRACY YARDLEY!
Inker: JIM AMASH
Lettering: JOHN WORKMAN
Coloring: JASON JENSEN
Editor: MIKE PELLERITO
Managing Editor: VICTOR GORELICK • Editor-in-Chief... RICHARD GOLDWATER
Special thanks to ROBERT LEFFLER and DYNA LOPEZ at SEGA Licensing

SONIC THE HEDGEHOG
--YOUR DOOM COMES AT THE HANDS AND TENTACLES OF... CROCTOBOT!
BWA HAHAHA! NO! STOP! TIME-OUT!
LAMEST--
--BADNIK--
--EVER!
HEY! I'M TERRIFYING!
NO WAY! I BEAT BOTH OF YOU BACK IN THE DAY!*
AHHA HAHAHA HAHA!!!
* WITH A LITTLE BIT OF HELP! SEE SONIC SELECT VOL. 8 FOR MORE!
YOU WILL FEAR ME!
WHOA! COME ON, SONIC, GET A GRIP!
HEE HEE HEE! OKAY, OKAY, CLAWS AND TENTACLES! HAW!!!
SMASH

YOU'VE... CHANGED!
FOR THE BETTER, BABE. NO MORE LAME *"EVIL TWIN"* SHTICK FOR ME.
YOU'LL BE THROWN OUT JUST AS EASILY.
TRY THAT AGAIN, OLD MAN.

MAN-O-MAN! LOOK AT HIM GO!
YEAH, HE'S PRETTY QUICK!
HEY, FIONA! WE'LL BE ON OUR WAY.
BEAN! BARK!
YOU TRY TO BLOW UP MY BOYFRIEND AND THEN DECIDE YOU CAN JUST WALK OUT?
WELL, *DUH.* I WAS GOING TO ASK IF YOU WANTED TO COME ALONG. HAVE SOME FUN LIKE THE OLD DAYS.
I CAN'T! I... I'M A FREEDOM FIGHTER NOW!
SUUUUUUURE YOU ARE! WELL, WHATEVER! TELL NIC I SAID "*HEY*" IF YOU SEE HER AGAIN!

HOLD ON! WE DO WHAT IT TAKES, BUT WE DON'T KILL.
OH, COME ON, ROUGE...
YOU WANT TO RUN WITH ME? THEN NO BODY COUNT.
SPOIL-SPORT. FINE. I'VE GOT A WUSS TO CRUSH.
SONIC? HOW DO YOU PLAN ON GETTING TO KNOTHOLE THAT FAST?
JUST FOLLOWING MY INSTINCT, BABE.
LET'S SEE IF INTUITION PANS OUT.
CHAOS CONTROL!

OH--NOW WHAT?
IS THAT ...CHAOS CONTROL?
ROUGE! AND...UM...
EVIL SONIC? ANTI-SONIC? OLD NEWS. THE NEW HOTNESS IS A REAL SCOURGE.
SOME FUR-DYE AND A NEW JACKET MAKE YOU TOUGH?
A SAMPLING OF THE MASTER EMERALD MAKES ALL THE DIFFERENCE.
DUDE. KNUCKLES WON'T LIKE THAT.
I'LL HANDLE HIM THE SAME AS HIS OLD MAN.
I HAPPEN TO LIKE KNUX'S DAD. I'LL STOMP YOU ON HIS BEHALF.
BRING IT ON, PUNK.
VIP!
HOLD ON, BLAST IT!

I STILL FUNCTION!
YOU'RE DOING NOTHING TO HELP SHADOW! I SHALL REPORT YOU AS A TRAITOR TO DR. ROBOTNIK!
NO. YOU WON'T.
QUICK TRUCE TO FINISH THIS UP?
WORKS FOR ME.
NOOOOO!

RECORD TIME! NICE WORK, FAKER.
HMPH!
NOW THEN...
...THE REASON WE'RE ALL HERE!
POW
URGH! CHEAP SHOT!
HA! AT LAST! EAT TURF, BLUE!
GUH!

ENOUGH. I HAVE A QUESTION...
YOU WANT A PIECE OF THIS, TOO, STRIPES?
GRAVE MISTAKE!
WHOOSH!

HA! TWO FOR TWO!
YOU'VE ASSURED YOUR MASCULINITY. CAN WE GET BACK TO THE MASTER EMERALD NOW?
I THINK WE NEED TO DOUBLE OUR ODDS, SHADOW.
FOR THE MOMENT.
BRING ALL YOU CAN! I'LL DISH IT BACK DOUBLE!
B-B-BRING IT...!
WHOA!
SKYOW

WHACK
HA! TOLJA... I'D...
GO DOWN, ALREADY!
WE'VE STOOD BY LONG ENOUGH!
THWACK
UGH!
GIT HIM!
GRR...
OKAY, YOU'VE HAD YOUR FUN. WE'RE OUT OF HERE.
HURRY AND TELEPORT US BACK TO ANGEL ISLAND.
I NEED A CHAOS EMERALD FOR THAT.
BRILLIANT!
JUST HOLD TIGHT!

THANKS FOR THE CAVALRY CHARGE.
BETTER LATE THAN NEVER.
SHADOW, ARE YOU...?
STEP ON IT, SCOURGE! SHADOW LOOKS TICKED!
MAYBE IF I DIDN'T HAVE THE DEAD-WEIGHT TO TOW...!
WHAT THE-- WHERE DID THIS COME FROM?
DON'T QUESTION IT, JUST BE THANKFUL! QUICK! INSIDE!
FWASH

SO MUCH FOR YOUR NEW BASE OF OPERATIONS.
I PROMISE SONIC, WE'LL HAVE A BETTER DEFENSE SYSTEM ONLINE SOON!
AND SO MUCH FOR YOUR BIRTHDAY.
ARE YOU GUYS KIDDING? EVERYTHING WORKED LIKE A CHARM!
THE BASE DREW ALL OF ROBOTNIK'S FIRE FROM KNOTHOLE--AND OUR FAMILIES. WE'RE ALL OKAY AFTER THREE ATTACKS. OKAY, MAYBE I GOT ROUGHED UP A BIT, BUT I LIVE FOR THIS STUFF!
WE'VE RECOVERED FROM WORSE, AND WE CAN DO IT AGAIN. WE'RE THE FREEDOM FIGHTERS.

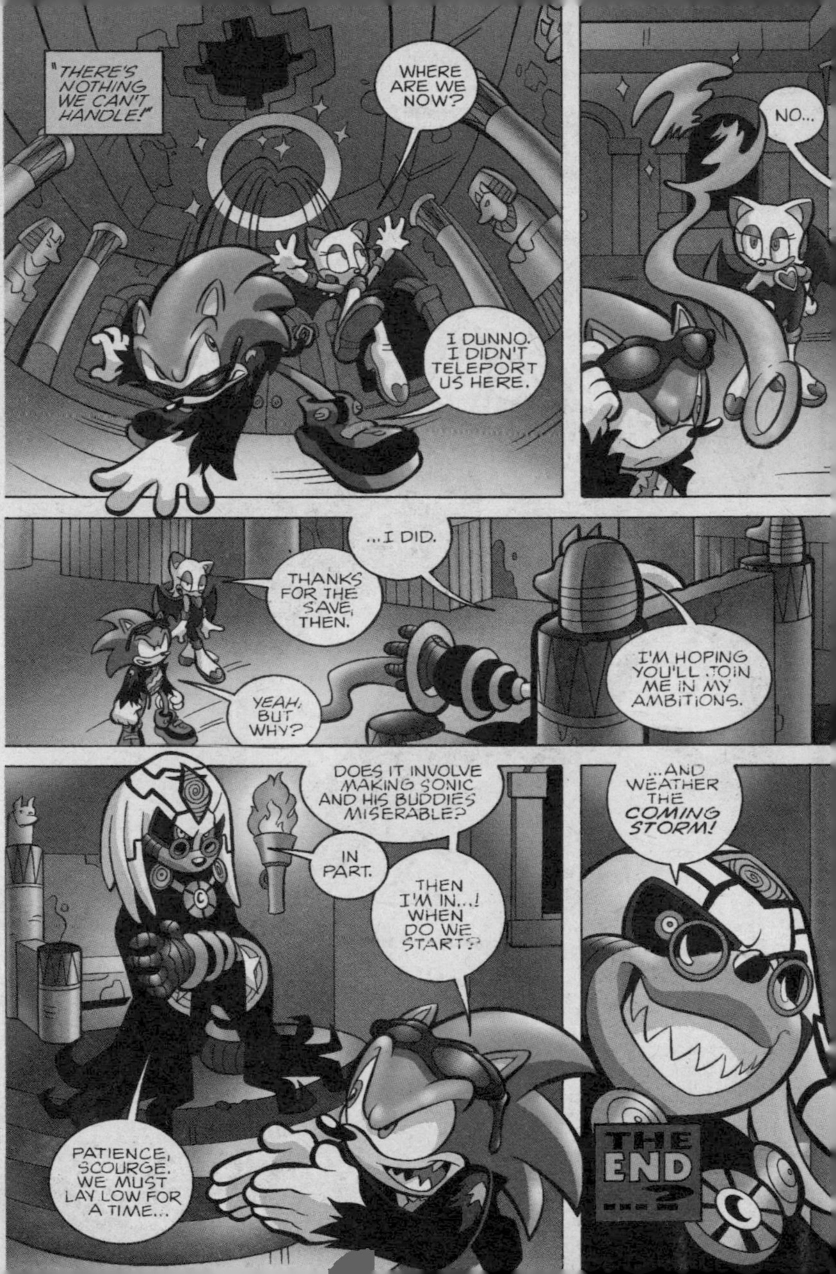
"THERE'S NOTHING WE CAN'T HANDLE!"
WHERE ARE WE NOW?
I DUNNO. I DIDN'T TELEPORT US HERE.
NO...
...I DID.
THANKS FOR THE SAVE, THEN.
YEAH, BUT WHY?
I'M HOPING YOU'LL JOIN ME IN MY AMBITIONS.
DOES IT INVOLVE MAKING SONIC AND HIS BUDDIES MISERABLE?
IN PART.
THEN I'M IN...! WHEN DO WE START?
PATIENCE, SCOURGE. WE MUST LAY LOW FOR A TIME...
...AND WEATHER THE COMING STORM!
THE END ?

SONIC SUPER DIGEST
PIN-UP PAGE!
PEPPERS
JOUSPIN
JENSEN

ARE THEY MEN...OR MONSTERS?
UNIVERSAL STUDIOS
HOME OF THE ORIGINAL
MONSTERS™
LON CHANEY AS QUASIMODO
The Hunchback of Notre Dame (1923)
BORIS KARLOFF AS
DR. JEKYLL/MR. HYDE
TRANSFORMS FROM
JEKYLL TO HYDE!
UNIVERSAL MONSTERS SELECT
ACTION FIGURES SERIES 4
DIAMONDSELECTTOYS.COM
UNIVERSAL
A COMCAST COMPANY
DIAMOND SELECT TOYS
Chaney ENTERTAINMENT
COMIC SHOP LOCATOR SERVICE
comicshoplocator.com
www.diamondselecttoys.com

CRY FREEDOM!
YOUR ATTENTION, PLEASE!
EVERYONE IN THIS TOWN IS NOW THE PROPERTY OF THE EGGMAN EMPIRE! RESISTANCE WILL BE MET WITH MOCKING LAUGHTER AND VIOLENCE, NOT NECESSARILY IN THAT ORDER!
FURVILLE --NOW.
WRITER: IAN FLYNN
PENCILS: TRACY YARDLEY!
INKS: TERRY AUSTIN
COLORS: MATT HERMS
ASSISTANT EDITOR: VINCENT LOVALLO
EDITOR/EXEC. DIRECTOR OF EDITORIAL: PAUL KAMINSKI
VICTIMS WILL BE ROBOTICIZED AND MADE MY TIRELESS, THANKLESS SLAVES. THOSE WITH THE PESKY IMMUNITY WILL INSTEAD BE LEGIONIZED, CONSCRIPTED INTO MY ARMY AND USED TO HUNT DOWN THEIR LOVED ONES. IF YOU HAVE A PREFERENCE, PLEASE INFORM THE EGG-SWATS AS THEY BEAT YOU INTO SUBMISSION! WHA HA HA HA!

AAAAND OUT! THAT WILL DO FOR NOW!
ABOUT THAT "IMMUNITY," BOSS--I THOUGHT YOU TOOK CARE OF IT WITH THE COSMIC RESET BUTTON?*
NO, UNFORTUNATELY. THANKS TO THOSE MEDDLING ALIENS, HALF THE PLANET IS STILL IMMUNE TO MY ROBOTICIZER.** BUT THAT STILL LEAVES PLENTY TO SUBJUGATE!
*STH #225. **STH #123.
YEAH... BUT AIN'T THE ROBOTICIZER BUSTED?***
INDEED. AND IN ADDITION TO THAT, WE'RE DANGEROUSLY LOW ON FUEL AND SUPPLIES AFTER OUR RECENT OUTINGS.**** WHY ARE WE MAKING THIS DETOUR ON OUR WAY TO THE SHAZAMAZON BASE?
***STH #230. ****STH #230-234.+ SU #37-40 (THE EGGMAN ARC!)
FIRSTLY, I'LL GET AROUND TO FIXING THE ROBOTICIZER. THEY CAN ROT IN PRISON EGGS UNTIL THEN. SECONDLY, FURVILLE MANAGED TO SURVIVE ONE ATTACK ALREADY, AND I WON'T STAND FOR SUCH AN INSULT.*****
GONK!
*****STH #119 --THEY NARROWLY AVOIDED EGGMAN'S ATTACK, THANKS TO SONIC AND TAILS!
WITH NEW MOBOTROPOLIS SURVIVING MULTIPLE ATTACKS, I HAVE TO MAKE AN EXAMPLE OUT OF SOMEWHERE TO CRUSH ANY INSIPID NOTIONS OF "HOPE." I DON'T NEED ANY NEW HEROES SHOWING UP...
AND MOST IMPORTANTLY--IT'S ONE OF THE LARGEST SETTLEMENTS ON THE CONTINENT.
****** MY GOSH, IT'S FULL OF STARS! ALL THESE COMICS AND MORE CAN BE FOUND ON THE SONIC COMICS APP!

"...NOW THAT THE FREEDOM FIGHTERS HAVE BEEN BROKEN."
FREEDOM HQ-- EARLIER.
AND IT'S NOT THE FIONA THING, OR THAT I'M BETTER LOOKING..."
...IT'S THAT ALL IT TAKES IS ONE BAD DAY, AND YOU'D BE JUST LIKE ME.
SONIC! ARE Y-- THERE HE IS! WE'VE BEEN LOOKING ALL OVER FOR YOU!
BUNNIE'S GONE!
SHE LEFT US A LETTER, BUT DIDN'T SAY WHERE SHE WAS GOING!*
* SONIC #235
I KNOW.
YOU ALREADY --? THEN WHAT DO WE DO ?!
SALLY'S BEEN ROBOTICIZED, THE CITY'S TURNED AGAINST NICOLE, ANTOINE'S IN A COMA, AND BUNNIE'S MISSING! THE TEAM IS FALLING APART!
"FALLING APART"? DUDE, THE DOC BEAT US. NAUGUS IS KING. THE FREEDOM FIGHTERS ARE DONE. SO...

CUT IT OUT! WE DON'T HAVE TIME FOR THOSE KINDS OF JOKES!
WAP
BECAUSE YOU *ARE* JOKING, RIGHT? BECAUSE YOU'D *NEVER* QUIT, ESPECIALLY WHEN YOUR FRIENDS NEED YOU MOST-- *RIGHT?*
WE DIDN'T LEARN TO BE FREEDOM FIGHTERS FROM JUST ANYONE, Y'KNOW.
YOU DIDN'T QUIT WHEN YOU GOT ARRESTED. YOU DIDN'T QUIT WHEN ROBOTNIK CAME BACK. YOU DIDN'T QUIT WHEN WE LOST OLD MOBOTROPOLIS, OR KNOTHOLE, OR OUR FAMILIES, OR ANY OTHER TIME! SO GET UP! WE'VE GOT FREEDOM FIGHTERS TO SAVE!
YOU'RE RIGHT, AMY. I'M NOT GOING TO LET IT ALL GET TO ME. AND IT'S GOOD TO KNOW YOU TWO ARE STILL IN THIS ALL THE WAY. WHAT I WAS GOING TO SAY...
...IS WE LOST THE OLD F.F., SO WE'VE GOT TO COME UP WITH SOMETHING *NEW.* WE'RE GOING TO HAVE TO SERIOUSLY BRAIN-STORM, THOUGH. WE'RE IN *ROUGH* SHAPE, AND WE'VE GOT A LOT ON OUR PLATE RIGHT NOW.
I HATE TO PILE IT ON...

...BUT IT JUST GOT WORSE TODAY.
YO--I DIDN'T EVEN KNOW YOU WERE HERE. AREN'T YOU SUPPOSED TO BE WORKING WITH THE COUNCIL RIGHT NOW?
THAT'S THE THING. I'VE RESIGNED OUT OF PROTEST.
...THIS IS THAT "GETTING WORSE" THING, ISN'T IT?
UH-HUH.
OKAY-- I'LL BITE--
--WHY?
THE COUNCIL APPROVED KING NAUGUS' ORDER TO HAVE NICOLE EXILED FROM THE CITY'S SYSTEMS.
WHAT ?!
YOU MEAN MY M... SHE VOTED FOR THIS?!
I JUST FINISHED TOUCHING UP OUR SERVER FOR HER HERE TO GIVE HER A LITTLE MORE "ROOM," I WISH IT WAS AS SOPHISTICATED AS HER HAND-HELD FORM, BUT...
ONE STEP AT A TIME, ROTE. ON THE BRIGHT SIDE, THAT MEANS WE GET YOU BACK ON THE ACTIVE ROSTER, RIGHT?
RIGHT. EXCEPT WITH JUST THE FOUR OF US, WE CAN'T KEEP WATCH OVER THE CITY AND CHASE DOCTOR EGGMAN...

"LIKE YOU SAID--WE HAVE TO COME UP WITH SOMETHING NEW."
RUN
AAAAAAH
HELP
FURVILLE --NOW.
WHICH WAY DO WE GO?
THIS WAY! WE'LL SLIP OUT ALONG THE EDGE OF TOWN, AND--
TARGETS ACQUIRED!
GO! GO!
ALL WILL SERVE THE MASTER.

SEARCH TEAMS REPORT 70% OF THE CITIZENS DETAINED. RESIST-ANCE IS LESS THAN EXPECTED.
AND WITH NO FREEDOM FIGHTERS GETTING IN THE WAY FOR ONCE... HOW ...*REFRESHING.*

NEW MOBO-TROPOLIS--EARLIER...
...AND SINCE THE OLD FREEDOM FIGHTER FORMULA WON'T CUT IT, WE WANT TO SPLIT INTO TWO TEAMS. I'LL LEAD THE FIRST ONE, HUNT DOWN OL' BUTTNIK, AND RESCUE SALLY.
WHICH LEAVES ME IN COMMAND OF THE OTHER TEAM TO HELP PROTECT THE HOME FRONT. I THINK YOU ALL KNOW MY RESUME.
NOBODY DOUBTS YOUR LEADERSHIP EXPERIENCE OR BRAVERY. BUT... WHAT ABOUT YOUR BACK INJURY?
GOOD QUESTION.
THIS BATTLE SUIT PROVIDES CORRECTIVE SUPPORT AND PUTS ME BACK IN ACTIVE DUTY, NO PROBLEM.
AND YOU REALLY THOUGHT YOU COULD RETIRE FROM THE HERO THING...

THERE IS NO NEED FOR THESE TEAMS, QUICKSTER. *I* PROTECT THIS CITY. MOTION DENIED.
WE *VOTE* ON MOTIONS HERE, *SIRE*. EVEN IF WE'RE STILL ONE CHAIR SHORT. ALL IN FAVOR OF THE FORMATION OF THE NEW TEAMS?
IT NEVER HURTS TO HAVE BACK-UP, *SIRE*. YEA.
WELCOME BACK TO ACTIVE SERVICE, ROTOR, YEA.
YEA.
I LIKE THAT YOU WENT THROUGH THE PROPER CHANNELS THIS TIME. YEA.
YEA!
IF SUCH IS THE *WILL* OF THE *COUNCIL* ...THE MOTION *CARRIES*.
WHO WILL STAY BEHIND AND BE ON YOUR TEAM, ROTOR?
ACTUALLY, TAILS IS HELPING ME BRING TWO FORMER-CHAOTIX OUT OF "RETIREMENT" TO JOIN **TEAM FREEDOM** FIRST. THEN I PLAN ON HOLDING A RECRUITMENT DRIVE HERE IN THE CITY.
"TEAM FREEDOM," *HMM?* AND WHAT ABOUT YOU, SONNY-BOY?
I'M TAKING AMY AND TAILS FOR MY TEAM. WE'LL TRAVEL LIGHT, HIT HARD 'N' FAST, BRING SOME HOPE TO MOBIUS. AND AS YOU PROBABLY GUESSED, WE'RE CALLING OURSELVES...

SMASH
BLAM
SORRY WE'RE RUNNING SO LATE, EVERY-ONE!
YOU'RE IN GOOD HANDS NOW. JUST LEAVE EVERY-THING TO...
...TEAM FIGHTERS!
FURVILLE-- NOW.

WHA--?! N--?! THAT'S NOT FAIR!
HOW MANY MORE OF YOUR FRIENDS DO I NEED TO DESTROY BEFORE YOU GIVE UP, RODENT?!
I WON'T STOP UNTIL I'VE SAVED EVERYONE YOU'VE CAPTURED! I'LL NEVER STOP UNTIL I'VE HONORED THE SACRIFICES OF EVERYONE WHO'S FALLEN ALONG THE WAY! AND I WON'T BE THROUGH UNTIL I'VE KICKED YOUR FLABBY BEHIND ONCE AND FOR ALL!
SO YOU JUST KEEP PUSHIN' ME, DOC! I'LL PUSH RIGHT BACK!

BIG TALK. BUT ONLY TALK. SURRENDER TO THE MASTER.
SORRY, SAL...
BUT I CAN'T PULL MY PUNCHES WITH YOU! IT'S LIKE HOW YOU PULLED OUT ALL THE STOPS WHEN I GOT ROBOTICIZED...*
*SONIC ARCHIVES VOLUME 10 AND SONIC SELECT VOLUME 2.
'COURSE I WAS A WAY-COOLER-LOOKING ROBOT...
SONIC? SWEETIE? LESS BANTER, MORE SAVING FOLKS, PLEASE!
WOULD YOU QUIT NAGGING ME? SAL IS LEADING THE GROUND TROOPS! I AM SAVING FOLKS!
I'M NOT NAGGING!

PIKO
COME ON! IF THE THREE OF THEM CAN FIGHT FOR OUR HOMES, SO CAN WE!
YEAH! THAT'S THE WAY TO DO IT!
WE'RE RAPIDLY LOS-ING PRISONERS AND GROUND FORCES, BOSS. BY MY ESTIMATE, IF WE LEAVE NOW, WE'LL HAVE JUST ENOUGH POWER TO ESCAPE AND RE-FUEL IN--
FINE!
FULL RETREAT! BRING IN MECHA SALLY, BUT LEAVE THE EGG-SWATS TO COVER US!
FINALLY! I'M FREE!

ORDERS RECEIVED. RETURNING TO BASE FOR SHAZAMAZON OBJECTIVE.
OH, NO, YOU DON'T! YOU'RE GETTING RESCUED WHETHER YOU LIKE IT OR NOT!
GAK! TAILS! BRING HER DOWN!
ALL GROUND UNITS, PROVIDE COVER FIRE AT THESE COORDINATES IN THREE, TWO...
...ONE. RETURNING TO BASE.
IT'S NO GOOD, SONIC. THEY'RE GETTING AWAY!
DON'T SWEAT IT. I HEARD WHERE THEY'RE HEADED.

YOU'LL REMEMBER THE PLACE. NOW HELP US FINISH UP THE LAST OF THE ROBOTS. THE SOONER WE SAVE FURVILLE, THE SOONER WE CAN MOVE ON.
ROGER THAT!
WHEW! THAT'S MOST OF 'EM. THE CITIZENS ARE REALLY HELPING OUT.
YEP. ALL THEY NEEDED WAS A LITTLE INSPIRATION FROM THE RIGHT HEROES.
BET I CAN TAKE OUT MORE STRAGGLERS THAN YOU CAN!
YOU'RE ON!
The FREEDOM FIGHTERS are no more ... Long live TEAM FREEDOM and TEAM FIGHTERS! DOCTOR EGGMAN is on the run, but that doesn't mean he can't stir up MORE TROUBLE! Until then, enjoy SONIC UNIVERSE, SONIC SUPER SPECIAL MAGAZINE, and the GRAPHIC NOVEL LIBRARY!

LEADER OF THE BAND
Writer: IAN FLYNN
Pencils: TRACY YARDLEY!
Inks: TERRY AUSTIN
Colors: MATT HERMS
Letters: JOHN WORKMAN
CITIZENS OF NEW MOBO-TROPOLIS! AFTER CON-SIDERING ALL THE VOLUNTEERS (ALL TWO OF THEM), I PRE-SENT YOUR DEFENDERS OF FREEDOM AT HOME... TEAM FREEDOM!
TEAM FREEDOM RECRUITMENT! SERVE YOUR CITY TODAY!
HELLO, EVERYONE! WE'LL DO OUR BEST!
I HAVE TO ADMIT, VANILLA, I'M SURPRISED YOU'D ALLOW THIS. YOU WEREN'T VERY PLEASED THE LAST TIME CREAM HAD A LITTLE... ERM... ADVENTURE.*
I KNOW. I'M USED TO A QUIET LIFE, ROSIE, AND I WANT MY DAUGHTER SAFE. BUT AT THE SAME TIME, CREAM COULD NEVER PASS BY THE OPPORTUNITY TO HELP.
Ms. ROSE SAID CREAM HAS THE POTENTIAL TO BE A GREAT HERO, AND I BELIEVE HER.
*SU # 21-24.
THIS WAY, SHE CAN START OFF IN SAFETY. AFTER ALL, THE CHILDREN UNDER YOUR CARE TURNED OUT QUITE EXTRA-ORDINARY!
AYE, MY LITTLE CHARGES HAVE SAVED THE WORLD DOZENS OF TIMES OVER. I'M SURE YOURS HAS JUST AS BRAVE A HEART.

SO...
...THESE WILL BE OUR DEFENDERS, SHOULD THE DOCTOR ATTACK WITH UNYIELDING STEEL AND UNCARING FIRE?
YOU'D DEFEND US WITH BAD-NIKS? TWO WHO HAVE ATTACKED YOU IN THE PAST?
SALUTATIONS. WE ARE HAPPY TO RETURN TO SERVICE.
PING!
JUST AS YOU FOUGHT US BEFORE? HEAVY AND BOMB REBELLED AGAINST THE DOCTOR FIRST.* TAILS AND I RE-COVERED THEIR PRIMARY CORES AND REBUILT THEM.
*SONIC SELECT VOLUME 2.
THE REST OF THE CITIZENS BELIEVE I AM ENOUGH TO PROTECT THEM! THOSE WHO DON'T ARE--WHAT? --THIS CHILD AND THIS SIMPLETON?
MY NAME IS "BIG."
PFFT. YES. OF COURSE IT IS. SNRK
TELL THESE WELL-MEANING, MISGUIDED FEW THEY ARE UNNEEDED. MY PEOPLE, YOUR KING IS ALL YOU NEED!
WE ARE SANCTIONED BY THE COUNCIL AND ARE HERE TO HELP!
ONE MAN CAN'T PROTECT ALL OF NEW MOBO-TROPOLIS.

HE COULDN'T STOP THE BATTLE BIRD ARMADA FROM BLOWING A HOLE THROUGH THE HEART OF THE CITY!* AND IT'S THANKS TO NICOLE'S NANITES THAT WE HAVE OUR HOMES BACK AT ALL!
YOUR WORDS BORDER ON TREASON, WALRUS.
*"BABYLON RISING" SU # 33-36
RRUMMBLE!
AAAAH! RUN!
INCOMING!
SHUT UP! SHUT UP! LET ME WORK! WE'LL ALL BE CRUSHED--!

HEAVY! BIG! CATCH THE CIVIC CENTER!
OKAY!
CREAM! START AIR-LIFTING PEOPLE TO SAFETY! I'LL JOIN YOU IN A MINUTE!
RIGHT AWAY, SIR!
BE CAREFUL, DEAR.
CHEESE, THROW BOMB TOWARDS THE COLLAPS-ING ROOF. BOMB, I NEED A BLAST TO REDUCE THE RUBBLE AND BLOW IT BACK, GOT IT?
CHAO!
PING!
GOOD! ON MY MARK. THREE-- TWO-- ONE--
SHA-BOOM!

HOORAY! WOO-HOO! GO, TEAM FREEDOM!
EXCUSE ME?
NOTHING! JUST... TALKING TO MYSELVES, MYSELF!
GREAT WORK, GUYS! HOLD IT STEADY, AND I'LL DO WHAT I CAN TO STABILIZE THE NANITES.
NOW DO YOU SEE WHAT YOU'VE DONE? YOU'VE RUINED EVERYTHING!
BEHOLD! NICOLE'S NANITES BETRAY US AGAIN!
NICOLE'S NOT HERE! IF ANYTHING, SHE WOULD'VE PREVENTED THIS GLITCH BEFORE IT HAPPENED! I CAN DIRECT THE NANITES TO REBUILD FROM MY SUIT, BUT IT WOULD BE FASTER AND MORE EFFICIENT IF SHE WAS STILL WITH US!
GO, TEAM FREEDOM!
THEN I WILL INVESTIGATE THE EARTH BENEATH, MADE TREACHEROUS BY THE ARMADA'S ASSAULT!
AND, IN THE SHADOWS, PERHAPS FIND A MEANS TO SOLVE MY PROBLEMS OF THE COUNCIL AND THE FICKLE TEMPERAMENT OF MY PEOPLE!
WHAT EVIL IS KING NAUGUS PLANNING? FIND OUT IN SONIC UNIVERSE #41-44: THE SECRET FREEDOM FIGHTERS! AVAILABLE ON THE SONIC COMICS APP!

SONIC SUPER DIGEST
PIN-UP PAGE!

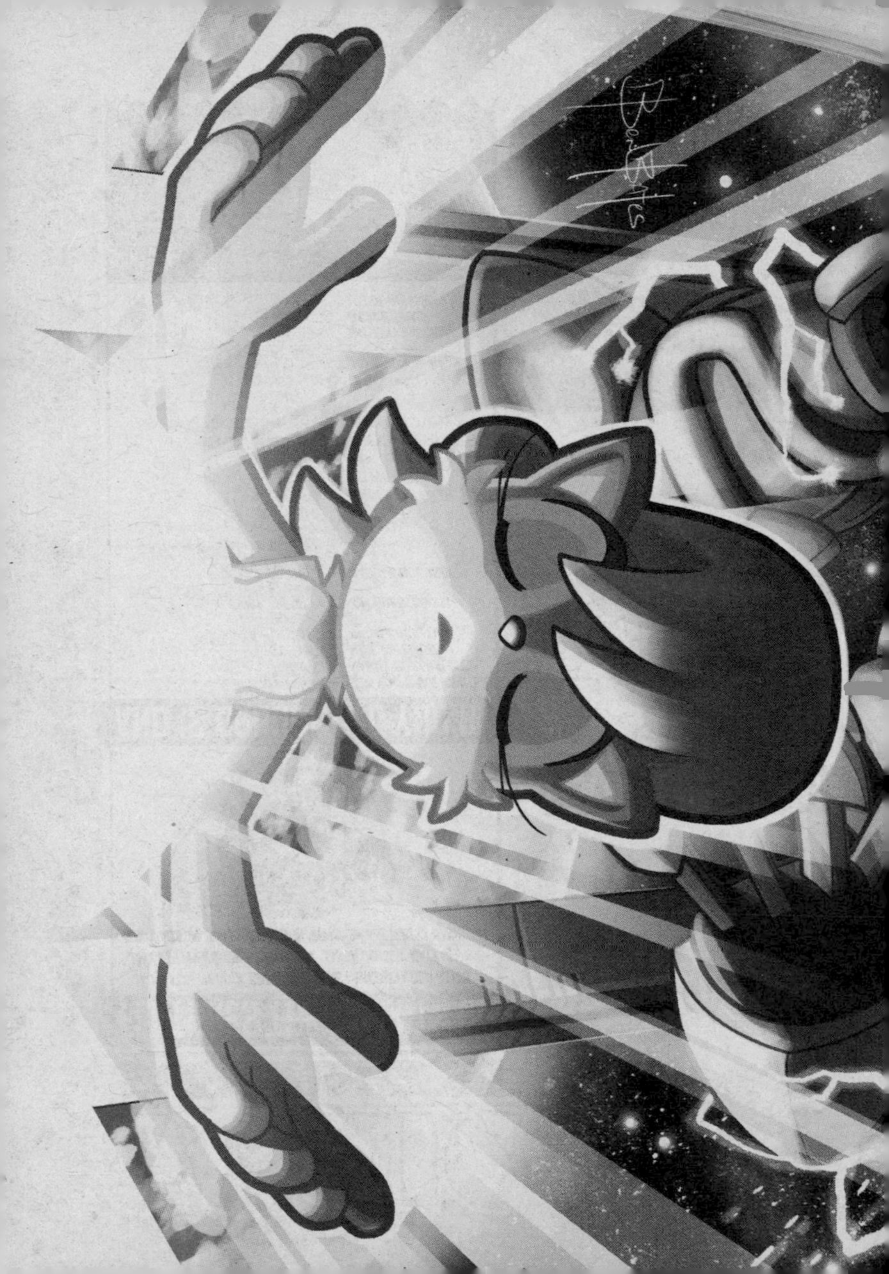

SONIC SUPER DIGEST

PRESENTS
The Sonic Spin!

FEATURES THE TALENTS OF

IAN FLYNN, PATRICK SPAZIANTE, TRACY YARDLEY!, BEN BATES, JAMAL PEPPERS, JONATHAN GRAY, JASON JENSEN, MATT HERMS, TERRY AUSTIN, JIM AMASH, JOHN WORKMAN and TERESA DAVIDSON

AND IS BROUGHT TO YOU BY

PUBLISHER/CO-CEO	JONATHAN GOLDWATER
CO-CEO	NANCY SILBERKLEIT
PRESIDENT	MIKE PELLERITO
CO-PRESIDENT/ EDITOR IN CHIEF	VICTOR GORELICK
SENIOR VICE PRESIDENT: SALES AND BUSINESS DEVELOPMENT	JIM SOKOLOWSKI
SENIOR VICE PRESIDENT: PUBLISHING & OPERATIONS	HAROLD BUCHHOLZ
VICE PRESIDENT: SPECIAL PROJECTS	STEVE MOOAR
EDITOR/EXECUTIVE DIRECTOR OF EDITORIAL	PAUL KAMINSKI
ASSISTANT EDITOR	VINCENT LOVALLO
PRODUCTION MANAGER	STEPHEN OSWALD
DIGEST EDITOR	CARLOS ANTUNES
SENIOR ART DIRECTOR	ELLEN LEONFORTE
DIRECTOR OF PUBLICITY AND MARKETING	STEVEN SCOTT
PROOFREADER	CARLY INGLIS
FEATURES CONTRIBUTIONS AND BOOK DESIGN	JONATHAN H. GRAY
SPECIAL THANKS TO	ANTHONY GACCIONE & CINDY CHAU @ SEGA LICENSING

FEATURED FAN ART

Ashley D.
from Texas

Toby B.
from Texas

NEXT TIME IN... SONIC SUPER DIGEST

SUPER PREVIEW

Episode Five!

JUMP FOR JOY!

Next issue leads off with a *BRAND NEW STORY* adapting SEGA's hit Sonic mobile game:

SONIC JUMP™

Don't walk ***or*** run! This time, ***JUMP*** like a blue hedgehog to your nearest comic store for your copy of **SONIC SUPER DIGEST *#5*!**

SEE YOU NEXT ISSUE!

CHECK OUT THESE TITLES ALSO COMING SOON!

A STICKER SPECTACULAR!

THE *SONIC SUPER SPECIAL MAGAZINE* IS BACK AND THIS TIME *WITH STICKERS!* PEEL AND STICK *YOUR* FAVORITE SONIC CHARACTERS ANYWHERE AND EVERYWHERE!

SONIC UNIVERSE#55 (On sale in AUGUST)
SONIC #252 (On sale in SEPTEMBER)
SONIC SUPER SPECIAL #8 (on sale in AUGUST)

Don't miss it!

SONIC SUPER DIGEST (2324-9552), No. 4, October 2013. Published quarterly by Archie Comic Publications, Inc., 325 Fayette Avenue, Mamaroneck, New York 10543-2318. Jonath Goldwater, Publisher/Co-CEO, Nancy Silberkleit, Co-CEO, Mike Pellerito, President, Victor Gorelick, Co-President. Single copies $3.99 in the U.S.; $4.59 in Canada. Subscription rate: U $15.96 for 4 issues; $18.36 in Canada. All Canadian orders payable in U.S. funds. SEGA, Sonic the Hedgehog and all related characters and indicia are either registered tradema or trademarks of SEGA CORPORATION © 1991-2013. SEGA CORPORATION and SONICTEAM, LTD./SEGA CORPORATION 1991-2013. All rights reserved. This product is manufactur under license from Sega of America, Inc., 350 Rhode Island St., Ste 400, San Francisco, CA 94103 www.sega.com. Nothing may be reprinted in whole or part without written permissi from Archie Comic Publications, Inc. This periodical may not be sold except by authorized dealers and is sold subject to the conditions that it shall not be sold or distributed with a part of its cover or markings removed, nor in a mutilated condition, nor affixed to or as a part of any advertising, literary or pictorial matter whatsoever. No actual person is named delineated in this fiction magazine and any similarities to real people and places in this fiction magazine are purely coincidental. Distributed in India by the Variety Book Depot, New De - 110 001. E-mail: varietybookdepot@rediffmail.com. Periodicals postage pending at the post office at Mamaroneck, New York and at additional mailing offices. Title registered in U Patent Office. POSTMASTER, send address changes to SONIC SUPER DIGEST c/o Archie Comic Publications, Inc., 325 Fayette Avenue, Mamaroneck, NY 10543-2318. Printed in US